Across the Curriculum GEOGRAPHY

for ages 9 – 10

Introduction

Across the Curriculum Geography provides a wide range of specially devised photocopiable worksheets, based on the QCA geography units, that can be used to address other curriculum areas when teaching geography. Alternatively, you may prefer to use the worksheets when teaching other subjects, in the knowledge that you are also covering valuable aspects of the geography curriculum.

For most of the units in this book there is a topic web and a set of Teacher's Notes. The topic web refers to possible links that can be made to other subjects, to help you with your planning, but you may well come up with more ideas and these can be added to the web as you go along. The Teacher's Notes provide background information on the worksheets and details of the Numeracy and Literacy and other curriculum objectives that each sheet covers. A summary of these objectives is provided on the Contents page overleaf.

Some sheets, which do not have a specific geographical content, are included because the geography topic provides obvious and important links to aspects of other subjects.

Many of the worksheets will be invaluable for speaking and listening – an important aspect of English in the National Curriculum that is not always addressed through the Literacy Strategy. Most of the worksheets can be used as a focus for small group activities and are ideal for children working with teaching assistants.

Contents and Curriculum Links

WORKSHEET	GEOGRAPHY	OTHER CURRICULUM OBJECTIVES
Water 1	2a	Literacy: Term 2 Word 9
Water 2	3a	Science: Investigative skills 1b, 2a, 2b, 2c, 2e, Materials and their properties 2a, 2b, 2d, 2e, 3a, 3b, 3c, 3e; Literacy: Term 1 Text 6 and 7, Term 2 Text 4; English: Speaking and Listening
Water 3	1a, 2b	Art: 1a, 1c, 2b, 2c, 4b, 5a, 5b, 5c, 5d
Water 4	2a	Music: 1a, 1c, 5b
Traffic in the high street 1	2a	Literacy: Term 2 Word 9, Term 3 Word 3, 12
Traffic in the high street 2	1a, 1b, 1c, 2b	Numeracy: Handling data
Traffic in the high street 3	1b, 3e	Literacy: Term 3 Text 18, 19
A contrasting locality 1	2c, 2d, 6a, 3g	
A contrasting locality 2	3c, 3g, 6a	Numeracy: Solving problems
A contrasting locality 3	1a, 2d, 3, 4, 5, 6, 7	
A contrasting locality 4	1a, 2d, 3, 4, 5, 6, 7	
A contrasting locality 5	1a, 2d, 3, 4, 5, 6, 7	
Traffic in our environment 1	2a, 2c, 2e, 5a	English: Speaking and Listening; Literacy: Term 1 Text 26, 27, Term 3 Text 17, 18, 19
Traffic in our environment 2	2a, 2c, 2e, 5a	English: Speaking and Listening; Literacy: Term 1 Text 26, 27, Term 3 Text 17, 18, 19
Traffic in our environment 3	2a, 2c, 2e, 5a	English: Speaking and Listening; Literacy: Term 1 Text 26, 27, Term 3 Text 17, 18, 19
Coasts 1	2c, 3b, 3c	Literacy: Term 2 Word 9
Coasts 2	2c, 3b, 3c, 3d, 4a, 4b, 6c	Literacy: Term 2 Word 9
Coasts 3	2c, 3b, 3c, 3d, 4a, 4b, 6c	Literacy: Term 2 Word 9, Term 3 Word 13
Coasts 4	2c, 3b, 3c, 3d, 4a, 4b, 6c	Literacy: Term 2 Word 9, Term 3 Word 13
What's in the news? 1	2c, 7b	Literacy: Year 5 Term 2 Text 19, 20, 22
What's in the news? 2	2c, 7b	Literacy: Year 5 Term 2 Text 19, 20, 22
Connections across the world 1	2a, 2c, 3b, 3c, 3g	Numeracy: Solving problems, Measures
Connections across the world 2	2a, 2c, 3b, 3c, 3g	Numeracy: Solving problems, Measures
Our whole world 1	2c, 3b, 3c	Literacy: Terms 1, 2 and 3 Word 3; History 12, 13
Our whole world 2	1b, 1c, 2d, 3a	Literacy: Term 1 Text 22, Term 2 Text 17
Our whole world 3	1b, 1c, 2d, 3a	Literacy: Term 1 Text 22, Term 2 Text 17
Our whole world 4	1b, 1c, 2d, 3a	Literacy: Term 1 Text 22, Term 2 Text 17
Our whole world 5	1b, 1c, 2d, 3a	Literacy: Term 1 Text 22, Term 2 Text 17
Geography and numbers 1	2c	Numeracy: Shape and Space
Geography and numbers 2	2c, 2e	Numeracy: Shape and Space
Geography and numbers 3	2c, 2e	Numeracy: Shape and Space

Water

This topic web shows possible curriculum links but we will not have thought of everything so you may like to add some of your own.

LITERACY
- Topic based vocabulary development (Worksheet 1)

NUMERACY
- Solving problems related to capacity

PE
- Water safety/ personal survival

MUSIC
- Song writing related to 'water' (Worksheet 4)

SCIENCE
- Enquiry based work
- Changing state – water as a solid, liquid, gas (Worksheet 2)

Water

ART
- Landscapes with a water focus (Worksheet 3)
- Use of water colour as a medium, eg in QCA art units: *Objects and meaning* or *A sense of place*
- Appreciation of the work of other artists

HISTORY
- Water usage in Victorian Britain

RE
- Understanding the importance of washing before prayer in the Muslim faith

Water

(QCA Unit 11: Water)

QCA Unit 11 provides clear guidance for completing this topic. The worksheets in this unit offer supplementary materials to enable you to extend the topic across different curriculum areas. You may also wish to make use of maps of the British Isles and of the world that appear later in this book.

Worksheet 1 (**LITERACY**) introduces some of the geographical vocabulary needed for this topic. The answers to the clues are as follows:
1. rain
2. flood
3. polluted
4. disease
5. downpipe
6. rivers
7. evaporate
8. gutters
9. cloud
10. irrigation
11. purify
12. sea

As an extension activity you may like to ask pupils to find other words related to those above:
> rain – rainwater, rain-guage, rainfall, etc;
> flood – flooding, floodwater, etc;
> polluted – pollute, pollution, etc.

Worksheet 2 (**SCIENCE** – Investigative skills) is a science-based sheet that focuses on filtration and evaporation – it should be used for a speaking and listening activity but we have provided lines for children to jot down some ideas. The children may be very resourceful and creative in their ideas. Questions 1 and 2 are theoretical only. In question 2 it is important to consider the idea of boiling water to reduce risk of disease – pupils should be told that water should be boiled for twenty minutes or more, not just 'brought to the boil'.

For question 3, if you wish, pupils can be given water with twigs, pebbles and sand in and access to appropriate filtration quipment to enable them to complete their own investigation.

In addition to the science in this worksheet there is also a very short, famous extract from *The Rime of the Ancient Mariner* by Samuel Taylor Coleridge (1772–1834) and a verse from *Rain* by Ebenezer Jones (1820–1860). Ask the children to explain what Coleridge means in the extract. Do they agree with Ebenezer Jones?

Worksheet 3 (**ART**) asks pupils to produce a picture based on their own area and is suitable for group use and for photocopying on to an OHP transparency. Ideally the pupils should be taken to a locality where water is a feature of the landscape. This visit would provide an ideal opportunity for discussion of safety near water.

This sheet also introduces children to a piece of art created by a professional artist, Rachel Thomas.* The painting features Great Yarmouth.

Worksheet 4 (**MUSIC**) asks pupils to write a 'water' song and guides them through the steps needed to achieve a successful result. Pupils may decide to write a cheerful song, for example concerning the delights of drinking clean water or swimming in it. However, some may create compositions about the problems faced in underdeveloped countries due to a lack of clean water.

*Reproduced by kind permission of Rachel Thomas

Water 1

Name: Date:

  In the box below are some words that are connected in some way with water. Follow the clues to complete the 'word river'.

> rain   gutters   flood   sea   evaporate   purify   disease
> polluted   rivers   irrigation   cloud   downpipe

1. This falls from the sky.

   2. Overflowing water, sometimes caused by heavy rains.

      3. Dirty water, especially that which is unfit to drink, is often described as …

         4. Water that is not fit for drinking can cause …

            5. Water from the roof goes down this to reach the ground.

               6. The Thames, Trent, Severn, Clyde and Tyne are all examples of these.

                  7. When water becomes a vapour it is said to …

                     8. Rain water from the roof flows along these.

                        9. A body of water particles in the air.

                           10. Getting water to fields to ensure that crops can grow.

                              11. Do this to water to make it safe to drink.

                                 12. Where most rivers end.

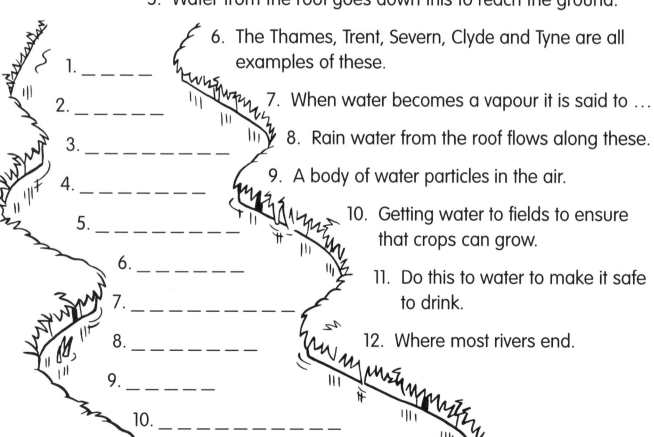

1. _ _ _ _
2. _ _ _ _ _
3. _ _ _ _ _ _ _
4. _ _ _ _ _ _ _
5. _ _ _ _ _ _ _ _
6. _ _ _ _ _ _
7. _ _ _ _ _ _ _ _ _
8. _ _ _ _ _ _ _
9. _ _ _ _ _
10. _ _ _ _ _ _ _ _ _ _
11. _ _ _ _ _ _
12. _ _ _

Water 2

Name: Date:

Here are two lines from *The Rime of the Ancient Mariner* by Samuel Taylor Coleridge:

> *Water, water everywhere,*
> *Nor any drop to drink.*

In extreme situations our comfort or our very survival can depend on our resourcefulness.

Look at Eric's problems below. Are you resourceful enough to help solve them?

> *Eric the explorer is bold and has no fears,*
> *Faced with tricky problems he needs your ideas.*

1. Eric has become becalmed at sea. His drinking water has run out. What can he do?

_____

_____

2. Eric has reached an uninhabited island. Think of three ways in which he may be able to get safe water to drink.

_____

_____

_____

3. Eric likes to wash his socks every day, but the water he has found in a pond nearby is full of twigs, pebbles and sand. How can Eric make the water clean enough to wash his socks in?

_____

_____

_____

> *More than the wind, more than the snow,*
> *More than the sunshine, I love rain;*
> *Whether it droppeth soft and low*
> *Whether it rusheth amain.*

> Ebenezer Jones

Water 3

Name: Date:

Most towns and villages developed where people could find water easily.

Think about 'watery' places near your school. These could include streams, rivers, ponds, lakes, waterfalls or even the sea.

You are going to create a picture based on a visit to one of these places.

- Sketch the place carefully.

- Make notes about the colours and shapes you can see.

- Notice how things that are further away seem smaller.

- It may help to take a photograph so that you remember what the place looks like. Remember, your picture does not have to look like a photograph.

- When you get back to school you can paint your water scene.

This picture was painted in Great Yarmouth by Rachel Thomas. It shows how an artist can create a successful picture without trying to make the painting look like a photograph.

Water 4

Name: Date:

Think about all you have learnt about water, particularly how different life would be without easy access to purified drinking water.

Work with a partner. Write a song with two or three short verses and a simple chorus. You can use a well-known tune if you like.

Here's how to do it:

1. Decide what the message in your song will be.

2. Write some verses in the same way that you might write rhyming poems.

3. Write a simple, easy to remember, chorus.

4. Now consider what sort of tune will best suit your words.

5. You may be able to write down your tune using musical notation but you could just practise singing it, then record it using a tape recorder.

6. If you have some instruments you could put a simple accompaniment to your song.

7. Perform your song to the class.

Traffic in the high street

This topic web shows possible curriculum links but we will not have thought of everything so you may like to add some of your own.

LITERACY
- Appropriate vocabulary for the topic
(Worksheet 1)
- Survey of people in the high street
(Worksheet 3)

MUSIC
- Write words appropriate to high street traffic issues, to the tune of *London's Burning* or other 'round' – perform these with simple accompaniments

NUMERACY
- Presenting data in graphical form
(Worksheet 2)

RE
- Places of worship on or near the high street – how people travel to these places

SCIENCE
- Keeping healthy – importance of walking whenever possible rather than using cars

Traffic in the high street

DT
- Bread – is there a bakery in the high street? Investigate type of bread made or sold there
- Bread making

HISTORY
- How roads were used in the town centre in Victorian times
- How traffic has developed in Britain since 1948

ICT
- Presenting data from survey work
- If appropriate, consider the use of traffic/pedestrian warning lights on the high street, leading to using a control box to make a similar model

Traffic in the high street

(QCA Unit 12: Should the high street be closed to traffic?)

Worksheet 1 (LITERACY) introduces appropriate vocabulary to be used when studying this unit. Pupils are encouraged to ensure that they understand the words provided.

Worksheet 2 (NUMERACY) asks pupils to collect and present data based on a practical traffic survey. Children will need to visit the high street to carry out this survey – obviously you will need the appropriate level of adult supervision and the children will need to be aware of the dangers associated with traffic and with strangers. Please refer to your school policies and local authority guidance on these issues. Provided all policies are followed strictly this activity is very worthwhile.

It is important to discuss whether the data would be likely to be the same at different times of the day or on different days of the week – ideally the survey could be carried out at different times. Pupils could make suggestions regarding how to explain the direction of the traffic that they are observing: eg North or South, left to right, from the traffic lights towards the post box, etc.

On return to school, the pupils can create graphs from the data that they have collected. This activity provides an excellent opportunity for discussion of mathematical issues relating to data handling: for example, that the graph needs a title and that both axes also need labels; the scale and calibration of the axes need to be decided, taking account the variety and amount of data to be illustrated.

What conclusions can pupils draw from the results of their surveys? A discussion of this is a vital part of the topic.

Worksheet 3 (LITERACY) is an instructional sheet concerning the design of a survey to discover when and why people use the high street and what changes, if any, they would like to see in this area. The children will need some guidance regarding the type of questions to use. Hopefully, in discussion they will offer a range of suggestions but you may need to prompt them with ideas for questions that are relevant to your own locality. These may include questions such as:

Do you live in the town?
How often do you visit the high street?
Do you think there is enough parking in the high street?
Do you think there is too much parking in the high street?
Do you think there is too much traffic in the high street?
Do you think that too many lorries use the high street?

After the children have designed their survey you could discuss the following:

- the best way to present their findings
- what the results tell them about how the high street is used
- what improvements could be made to the traffic flow
- any other improvements that could be made to the high street

Andrew Brodie: Across the Curriculum Geography 9–10 © A & C Black Publishers Ltd

Traffic in the high street 1

Name: Date:

Look at the pedestrian crossing below. It is full of words that you should understand and be able to spell. You can use these words when you are doing work about traffic in your local high street.

Write a clear simple definition for each word. The first one has been done for you.

You may need to use a dictionary to complete the task.

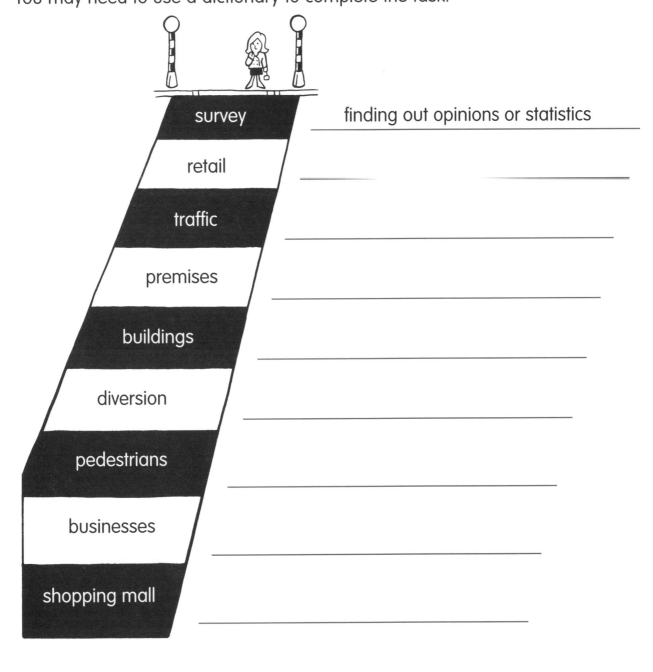

survey	finding out opinions or statistics
retail	
traffic	
premises	
buildings	
diversion	
pedestrians	
businesses	
shopping mall	

On a separate piece of paper put each of the words into a sentence about your locality.

Traffic in the high street 2

Name: Date:

You are going to do a survey of the amount and types of traffic in your high street. Some of you will count the vehicles going in one direction and some will count the vehicles travelling in the other direction, unless your high street is a one way street!

You must be sure to follow the safety instructions given by your teacher.

 Clip this sheet to a clipboard. Fill in the survey details and then complete your vehicle tally on the chart below.

Time of survey ————————— Date of survey —————————

Day of the week —————————

Direction of traffic ——————————————————————

Type of vehicle	Number of vehicles
car	
bus/coach	
van	
bicycle	
motorbike	
lorry	
other	

When you get back to school, create a graph to show your results.

Traffic in the high street 3

Name: Date:

You are going to design a survey to find out the way people use your local high street and what changes they think should be made.

Pay particular attention to their opinions regarding the traffic.

Points to note:

- Your questions should be designed to be answered in a minimum number of words.

- No very personal questions should be included. You don't wish to offend people.

- Space should be allowed for additional comments people wish to make.

- Consider how you are going to gather your information.

Questions	Answers and comments

A contrasting locality

(QCA Unit 13: A contrasting UK locality – Llandudno)

Although this topic provides useful links across the curriculum it is clearly based heavily on geography and accordingly we have not produced a topic web. Suggestions for possible linked activities are included on the following page. This unit provides an introduction to the study of Great Yarmouth and the surrounding area. The work takes into account that, although desirable, it is not always possible for pupils to undertake a field trip.

Worksheet 1 (LITERACY) invites pupils to complete some map work that should help pupils to understand Great Yarmouth's position in the country and why it has developed as a tourist destination.
Note: 'Norfolk' comes from 'North folk' of East Anglia.

Great Yarmouth is derived from the town at the mouth of the River Yare.

Worksheet 2 (LITERACY/NUMERACY) poses a range of questions about the Great Yarmouth locality, routes into the town, distance and travelling time from pupils' own locality.

Answers to questions 4–8:
4. The Norfolk Broads
5. North : Caister
   South : Hemsby
6. Anna Sewell
7. To find tourist attractions in the Great Yarmouth area, pupils could visit the official tourism web site: www.great-yarmouth.co.uk
8. A12, A47

Worksheets 3, 4 and 5 (LITERACY) comprise a series of pictures of the Great Yarmouth area. Each picture has text with it that explains a little about the photograph and poses a question for pupils to consider or investigate.

Notes on the photographs:
1. In early 2005 this was still Britain's largest offshore wind farm. The two other structures are 'Jack up drilling rigs'. These are towed to where they are needed and are used to drill holes when looking for hydrocarbons, such as oil, gas, etc.
2. The marker poles are to mark the deeper areas where craft will not run aground.
3. This picture includes the river and the town hall and shows some features that are also included in the painting by Rachel Thomas in the water section of this book.
4. The River Bure. The structure just visible in the background on the left hand side is Caister water tower. This is approximately 50 metres high and is visible for many miles around. It was constructed in the early nineteen-thirties. The photograph provides a starting point for an investigation of the Norfolk Broads.
5. The Rows were a feature unusual to Great Yarmouth. There are very few Rows left – many were destroyed in bombing raids during World War 2. The Rows were all built within the town walls.
6. Great Yarmouth has had a market for at least eight hundred years. The picture shows the market as it looked in 1906. The market is still thriving today in the same central area of the town. A visit to a market in your locality will give the children the opportunity to consider what a market consists of. What types of things are sold? Are they local products? etc.

A contrasting locality continued

Other interesting facts:

1. Both Charles Dickens and Daniel Defoe mention aspects of Great Yarmouth in their literature – Dickens in *David Copperfield* and Defoe in *Robinson Crusoe*.

2. Until the early fifteenth century the River Yare was crossed by ferry. The first bridge was built between 1415 and 1420.

3. Great Yarmouth has one of the only two purpose built circus buildings in England. This is called the Hippodrome.

4. Great Yarmouth was the original home of the 'fish finger' – this popular food was invented at the Bird's Eye factory. Note, there is no longer a Bird's Eye factory in the town.

5. A few miles along the coast south of Great Yarmouth is the town of Lowestoft which boasts the most easterly point in Great Britain.

Suggestions for additional curriculum links:

History – changes since 1948.

DT – investigate fun fairs in Great Yarmouth, leading to the making of simple moving models.

ICT – focused internet searches to find out about aspects of the locality.

Art – representing aspects of the town or its history with textile pictures.

A contrasting locality 1

Name: Date:

Mark the following features on the map:

   Label the town of Great Yarmouth;

   Label the town where you live;

   Shade the county of Norfolk yellow;

   Label the cities of Belfast, Cardiff, Edinburgh and London.

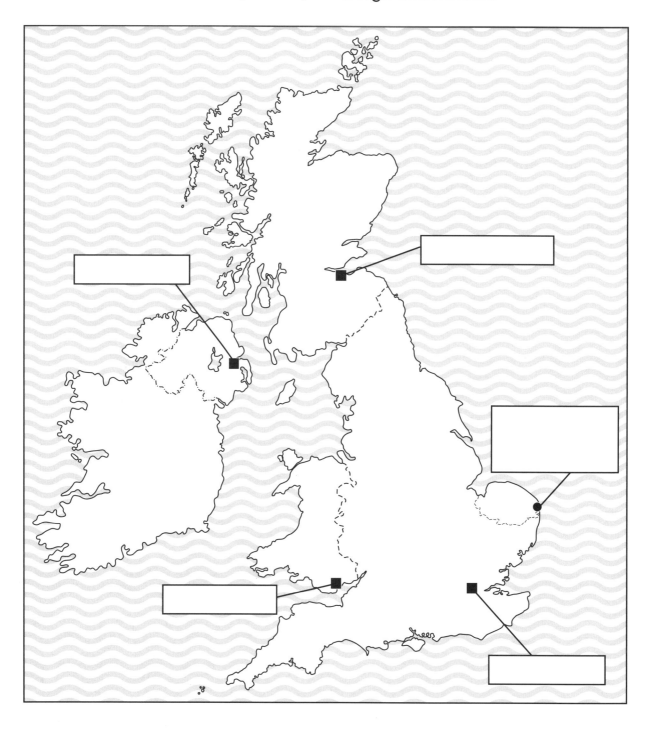

Andrew Brodie: Across the Curriculum Geography 9–10 © A & C Black Publishers Ltd

A contrasting locality 2

Name: Date:

You may need an atlas to help you with some of these questions. Access to the internet or tourist publications may help you to answer some of the others.

1. Approximately how far is it from your school to Great Yarmouth?

_____

2. If you travelled at an average speed of fifty kilometres per hour how long would a journey take from your school to Great Yarmouth?

_____

3. Describe the route from your school to Great Yarmouth.

_____

_____

_____

_____

_____

4. Name the National Park close to Great Yarmouth.

_____

5. Name the coastal towns immediately to the north and to the south of Great Yarmouth.

_____

6. Name the famous author born in Great Yarmouth. (Clue: she wrote *Black Beauty*.)

_____

7. Name two tourist attractions in the Great Yarmouth area.

_____

8. Name two main roads that reach Great Yarmouth.

_____

A contrasting locality 3

Name: Date:

On a sandbank called Scroby Sands, to the East of Great Yarmouth, there is an offshore wind farm which was Britain's largest when it was constructed in 2004.

If you look very carefully at the photograph you will see two other structures in the water. What do you think they are?

What forms of renewable energy can be found in your locality?

This picture, taken just to the north of Great Yarmouth centre, is of the River Bure. It joins the River Yare before it reaches the sea.

Find out which other rivers can be found in 'Broadland' and name some of 'The Broads'.

A contrasting locality 4

Name: Date:

This picture shows part of the River Yare shortly before it reaches the sea.
The large building to the left of the river is the town hall.

This is a picture of Breydon Water; it is part of the River Yare.

Why do you think
there are marker
posts in the
water?

A contrasting locality 5

Name: Date:

This is a picture of Market Row. This is one of the few remaining Rows but, at one time, Great Yarmouth had a network of one hundred and forty-five narrow streets called 'Rows'. They all ran from east to west and were so narrow that special carts known as 'troll carts' were made to transport things along them.

Can you find out more about the history of Great Yarmouth town?

This picture was taken in 1906 and shows the market in Great Yarmouth.

Is there a market in your town or a town nearby?

Traffic in our environment

(QCA Unit 20: Local traffic – an environmental issue)

A topic web has not been included for this unit as the possibilities will vary greatly depending on each individual locality.

Resources needed: A map of your local town showing existing river crossings and, if possible, the direction of traffic flow in this area.

Worksheets 1, 2 and 3 (**LITERACY**) are linked together.

Worksheet 1 is an instruction sheet suitable for group use or use with an OHP. It asks pupils to consider an additional river crossing for traffic in their nearest appropriate town. This has been chosen to complement the 'water' topic and builds on pupils' Year 4 work concerning why and how settlements develop, ie usually on a water course where crossing the river is possible.

Worksheet 2 asks pupils to present a formal written proposal with an appropriate plan.

Worksheet 3 is a further instruction sheet for class or group use and incorporates additional relevant activities that could be undertaken.

As extension activities:

1. Leaflets could be designed explaining the merits of the chosen proposal.

2. Letters could be written, as if to the local newspaper or town council, objecting to the proposed new river crossing.

Traffic in our environment 1

Name: Date:

Things to discuss:

- Look at a map of a local town.
  How does traffic cross the river?

- Discuss whether it would be a good idea to have another river crossing.
  If so, where would be the best place for it?

Things to consider:

- How would you use an extra river crossing to improve the traffic flow in the town?

- What type of river crossing would be best? You could consider a ferry or tunnel instead of a bridge.

- What problems might be caused by your proposals? For example, would it affect shops, pedestrians and other residents?

Presenting your proposal:

- Use Worksheet 2 to draw a map of the area around your new river crossing. Show the traffic flow on your map.

- Write a proposal for your new river crossing, in a clear impersonal style.

- Include all the reasons why your crossing should be constructed.

Andrew Brodie: Across the Curriculum Geography 9–10 © A & C Black Publishers Ltd

Traffic in our environment 2

Name: Date:

Names of proposers

_____   _____

_____   _____

Type of crossing proposed

_____

Name of river being crossed

_____

Name of town

_____

Written proposal

_____

_____

_____

_____

_____

_____

_____

_____

_____

_____

_____

_____

_____

_____

_____

My map

Traffic in our environment 3

Name: Date:

Your group will be given the opportunity to look at the proposal of each of the other groups. You will discuss the positive and negative points of each proposal.

You should also prepare to talk to the class about the merits of your group's proposal. You should be ready to answer difficult questions!

- Appoint a spokesperson for your group.

- Discuss ideas so that the spokesperson knows what to say.

- Don't blame the spokesperson if the class don't like your ideas!

When each group has presented their proposal and been questioned on it a vote can be taken to find out which proposal is the preferred option. No one should vote for their own scheme!

Proposal	Number of votes

Coasts

This topic web shows possible curriculum links but we will not have thought of everything so you may like to add some of your own.

LITERACY
- Appropriate technical vocabulary for the topic (Worksheet 1, 2, 3, 4)
- Use of the prefix 'trans'

ART
- Pictures that show movement – waves
- Studying landscape artists, including seascapes

NUMERACY
- Estimating numbers of grains of sand
- Weighing sand

ICT
- Digital photographs of coastlines
- Internet research in relation to coastlines

Coasts

SCIENCE
- Materials – sand, building on Year 3 work on characteristics of materials
- Earth, Sun and Moon – effect on tides

HISTORY
- The rise in popularity of coastal resorts in Victorian times
- Beach holidays in Britain since 1948

Coasts

(QCA Unit 23: Investigating coasts)

Schools can choose whether to study rivers or coasts and some teachers may choose to study both. We have included a unit on rivers and a further unit on coasts in *Across the Curriculum Geography for Ages 10-11.*

Worksheet 1 (**LITERACY**) consists of a blank map of the British Isles. This will be very useful for a wide range of geographical work in Year 5 but, for this worksheet, we suggest that you supply the children with the following vocabulary to enable them to label the map:

Countries: England, Northern Ireland, Republic of Ireland, Scotland, Wales;

Seas: North Sea, Irish Sea, English Channel, Atlantic Ocean, The Wash, Bristol Channel;

Geographical terms: estuary, firth, peninsula.

We suggest that the children label the South West of England as a peninsula, the mouth of the Thames as an estuary and the Firth of Forth as a firth. Note: 'firth' is a Scottish name for an estuary or inlet.

The pupils could shade the coastline carefully: the conventional method would be to shade outside the line marking the edge of the land area, using blue to represent the sea.

Worksheet 2 (**LITERACY**) consists of a map of Europe with international boundaries shown. Again, this map will be of use on many occasions. For this worksheet we suggest that you supply the pupils with the following vocabulary:

Countries: United Kingdom, France, Spain, Portugal, Switzerland, Belgium, Italy, Germany;

Seas: North Sea, Atlantic Ocean, Mediterranean Sea.

You may wish to include other countries on your vocabulary list. Again the pupils could shade the coastlines. The sheet can be used as a focus for discussion, using questions such as 'which country forms a peninsula in the Mediterranean Sea?' 'which country has no coastline?' 'which country is made up totally of islands?', etc.

Worksheet 3 (**LITERACY**) includes technical vocabulary for the topic on coasts. Some of the words will already be very familiar to the children but others are less frequently used geographical terms. Pupils are asked to match each word with its simple definition, then to rearrange the words in alphabetical order. You could ask the pupils to create a glossary for the topic using these words and others that arise during the course of your work.

Worksheet 4 (**LITERACY**) revisits the vocabulary from worksheet 3. We recommend that the children work in pairs, trying to decide in which box to place each word. They should find the 'man-made features' and the 'materials' boxes straightforward to complete but they will need to discuss some of the other words much more carefully.

Coasts 1

Name: Date:

The British Isles

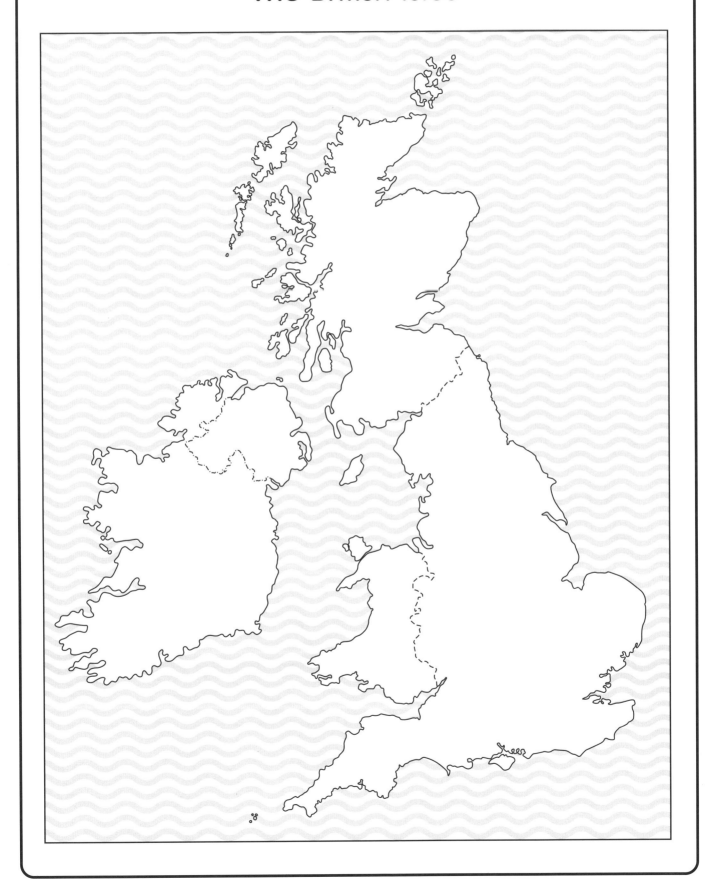

Coasts 2

Name: Date:

Europe

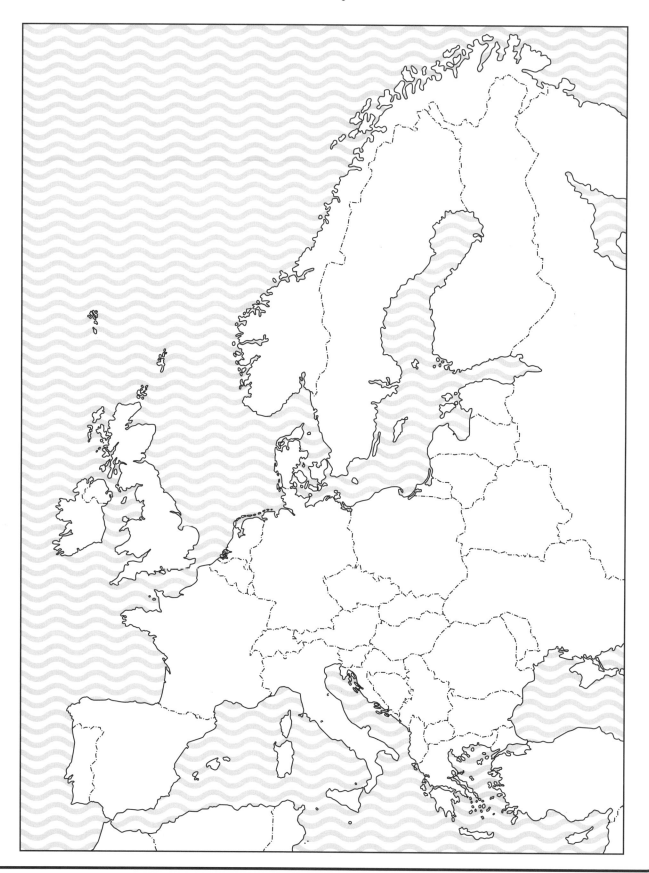

Coasts 3

Name: _____   Date: _____

✎ Match each word to its definition by joining them with a straight line

erosion	where the land meets the sea
sand	the process of moving material from one place to another
groynes	ridges of water that break on the shore
cliff	hard material that cliffs are made of
coast	a steep rock face
deposition	an area of sea that the land curves round
tide	pebbles on the sea-shore
cave	wooden fences built on a beach, at an angle to the sea, to reduce erosion
shingle	the wearing away of the land by water or wind
transportation	eroded material that has been dropped
beach	water in the sea that rises and falls regularly every day (caused by the gravitational pull of the sun and the moon)
waves	an area of land that sticks out into the sea, sometimes called a promontory
headland	a large area of land that sticks out into the sea and is almost surrounded by it
rock	a hollowed out section of the side of a cliff
bay	a sea-shore area of sand or shingle
peninsula	very fine grains of rock often found on the sea-shore

✎ Now rewrite the words in alphabetical order.

_____ _____ _____ _____

_____ _____ _____ _____

_____ _____ _____ _____

_____ _____ _____ _____

Coasts 4

Name: Date:

Look again at the words that you worked with on Worksheet 3.

Sort the words into categories by writing them in the correct boxes below.

physical features of the landscape

_____

_____

_____

_____

_____

_____

materials

_____

_____

_____

physical processes and their results

_____

_____

_____

_____

man-made features

_____

What's in the news?

(QCA Unit 16: What's in the news?)

We have not included a topic web for this unit as cross curricular links will depend on the news events studied.

For this unit the pupils will need access to a selection of newspapers or relevant websites. An alternative would be to use a recorded television or radio news broadcast, particularly if you wish to guide pupils towards particular news items.

Worksheets 1 and 2 (LITERACY) are linked sheets focusing on three news reports from different parts of the world. It is important for pupils to be given the opportunity to see differing accounts of the same news event, eg in different newspapers or newspaper and radio/television reports.

Worksheet 1 provides pupils with instructions as to how they complete worksheet 2. It can be used with a small group or could be photocopied on to a transparency for an OHP.

We have deliberately created worksheet 2 to allow pupils very little space – to be able to complete it they need to find the key point of each news story and they will have to write neatly and carefully.

You may wish pupils to label additional features on the map to reinforce other areas of study.

What's in the news? 1

LITERACY

Name: Date:

Look at some recent newspapers.

Find news reports about things that have happened in other parts of the world.

Choose three articles that you find interesting. Each article should concern an event in a very different location. For example, if one report is about an event in Australia then neither of the others should be.

- On Worksheet 2 there is a map of the world. Colour the British Isles red.

- Colour each of the countries where your news events are set using a different colour.

- Complete the key beside the map.

- Use the boxes below the map to write your own headline and a brief report about each event.

- Draw a straight line (using a ruler!) from the top of each news report box to the place on the map where the event happened.

Did you know that the key to a map is sometimes called the legend?

 Andrew Brodie: Across the Curriculum Geography 9–10 © A & C Black Publishers Ltd

What's in the news? 2

Name: Date:

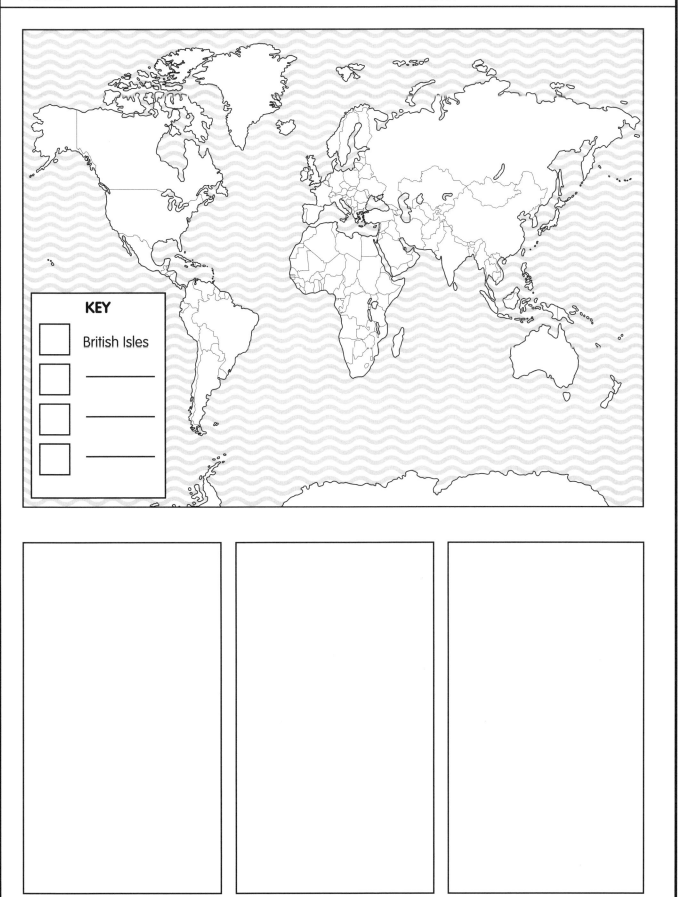

KEY

☐ British Isles

☐ _____

☐ _____

☐ _____

Connections across the world

CURRICULUM LINKS

This topic web shows possible curriculum links but we will not have thought of everything so you may like to add some of your own.

LITERACY
• Written descriptions of routes into Great Yarmouth
(Worksheet 1, 2)

NUMERACY
• Problem solving concerning distances and durations of journeys

ART
• Making a container to hold the picnic planned for the journey

Connections across the world

ICT
• Use of spreadsheet to show cost of return journey to Great Yarmouth, showing fuel costs/public transport costs, refreshments, etc

SCIENCE
• Planning picnic food for a journey, showing a balanced healthy meal

HISTORY
• How has Britain's road network changed since
a) Victorian times and/or
b) 1948?

Andrew Brodie: Across the Curriculum Geography 9–10 © A & C Black Publishers Ltd

Connections across the world

(QCA Unit 18: Connecting ourselves to the world)

Resources needed: Road atlases of Great Britain – you may be able to borrow these from parents.

As a step towards understanding connections across the world we have focused this work on journeys to Great Yarmouth, the town that we have used as our 'contrasting locality' in the British Isles.

To further extend this work you may like to consider air routes from other parts of the world. The closest airport to Great Yarmouth is at Norwich from where there are scheduled flights to Amsterdam - Amsterdam serves as a hub to other parts of the world. The next closest airports are at Stansted and Luton.

Please note that we have based this work around miles as opposed to kilometres as speed in 'miles per hour' rather than 'kilometres per hour' is still in common usage.

Worksheets 1 and 2 (LITERACY) are linked together.

Worksheet 1 is an instruction sheet suitable for individual or group use. Pupils are asked to mark the positions of three cities: Glasgow, Birmingham and Southampton. You may wish to add extra places to complement work undertaken in the classroom. They are asked to show routes from each of these places to Great Yarmouth, using motorways and 'A' roads. Pupils are then asked to describe one of these routes in writing, though you may choose to ask them to describe all three of the routes.

As an extension activity you could ask the children to find the mileage from each city to Norwich using the mileage chart that is usually provided in the front or back of the road atlas. You could also ask them to calculate how long each journey would take, assuming an average speed of 60mph on the motorways and 40mph on the A roads. This task could be simplified by using just one average speed to cover the complete journey. It is appropriate to point out that any long road journey is much safer when frequent stops are made.

INFORMATION:
Glasgow to Norwich = approximately 380 miles

Birmingham to Norwich = approximately 170 miles

Southampton to Norwich = approximately 205 miles

Connections across the world 1  LITERACY

Name: Date:

You will need a road atlas of Great Britain to complete this work.

1. Mark the following cities on the map on Worksheet 2. Then answer the questions below.

   Glasgow   Birmingham   Southampton

2. Discuss how you could get by road from each of these cities to Great Yarmouth. (Use the road atlas to work out a sensible route from each one. You should be able to reach Great Yarmouth using motorways and A roads.)

3. Look carefully at the road atlas. You will see numbers by each of the motorways; for example M4. You will also see numbers by each of the A roads; for example A27.

   Mark the route from each of the cities to Great Yarmouth on your map.

4. Colour the motorways blue and label them with their numbers.

5. Colour the A roads red and label them with their numbers.

6. Describe one of your routes using appropriate geographical vocabulary. For example: 'From Southampton travel north-east on the M3 …'

_____

_____

_____

_____

_____

_____

_____

_____

_____

_____

_____

_____

_____

Andrew Brodie: Across the Curriculum Geography 9–10 © A & C Black Publishers Ltd

Connections across the world 2

Name: Date:

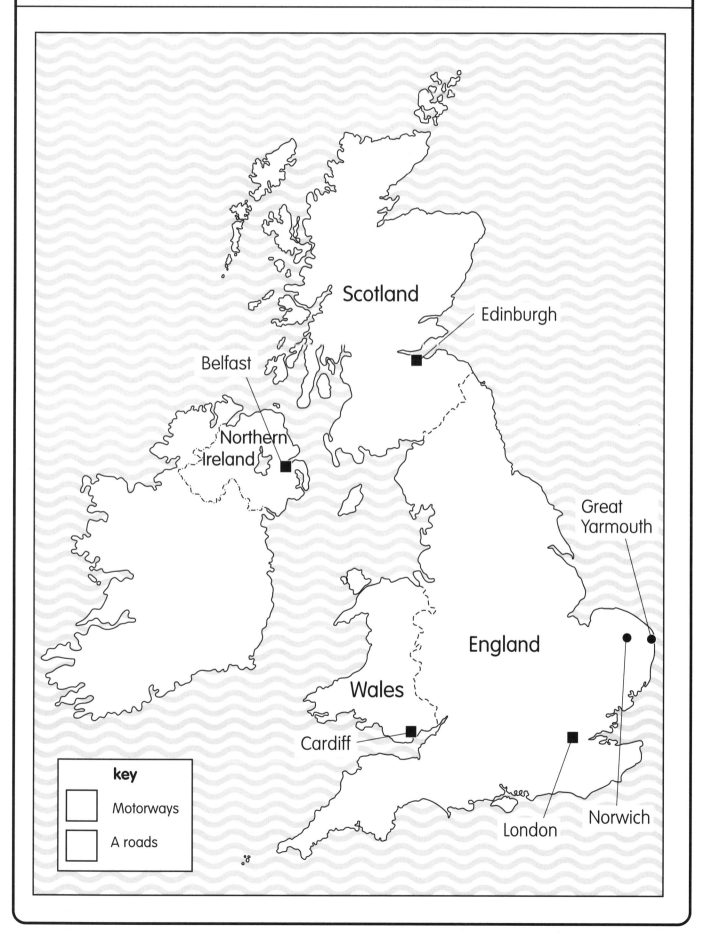

Our whole world

This topic web shows possible curriculum links but we will not have thought of everything so you may like to add some of your own.

DT
- Types of bread from around the world

LITERACY
- Vocabulary of names of some of the world's continents, oceans and countries
  (Worksheet 1)
- Use of capital letters for place names
- Reading clues about places
  (Worksheet 2, 3, 4, 5)

NUMERACY
- Comparisons of distances

ICT
- Potential use of web-cams for observing other parts of the world
- Finding information about places in the world through research on the internet

ART
- Landscape artists from other countries
- Costumes from around the world

Our whole world

HISTORY
- Indus Valley Civilisation
- Ancient Greece

RE
- Opportunities for discussion in relation to religious centres in the world, eg Mecca, Jerusalem
- The spread of world religions

MUSIC
- Chinese music, exploring pentatonic scales (note that not all music using pentatonic scales is Chinese)

PE
- Dance, using world music

 Andrew Brodie: Across the Curriculum Geography 9–10 © A & C Black Publishers Ltd

Our whole world

(QCA Unit 24: Passport to the world)

Worksheet 1 (**LITERACY**) is a map of the world. Pupils are required to write on the names of some countries and seas. They should also locate the British Isles, recognising the shape. The countries to be shown include:

Greece, as Ancient Greece is likely to be covered during Year 5;

Pakistan, as pupils may be studying the Indus Valley.

The other countries are:

United States of America (which can be shown as USA)

Australia

Brazil

Canada

Russia

China

Indonesia

Bangladesh

The seas are:

Atlantic Ocean

Pacific Ocean

Indian Ocean

Arctic Ocean

Caribbean Sea

Mediterranean Sea

We suggest that you write the names of the countries and seas on the whiteboard so that pupils can see them when completing this activity. Pupils can finish the map by lightly shading the land green and the sea blue.

Worksheets 2, 3, 4 and 5 (**LITERACY**) are all designed to address the QCA recommendation that pupils could participate in a game to identify a location when provided with two clues each day for a week – see QCA Unit 24: 'Passport to the world'. This is very time consuming for teachers so we are providing three sets of clues on sheets 2 to 4, then a pupil entry sheet on sheet 5. Sheet 2 gives clues about Mumbai; Sheet 3 about Sao Paulo; Sheet 4 about Athens. (Children could look up the meaning of the title 'philosopher'.)

Each sheet is designed so that you can photocopy it then cut the copy into five pieces, each containing two clues. You may decide to spread the games over the year, perhaps completing the Mumbai game in the autumn, Sao Paulo in the spring and Athens in the summer; or you may like to complete them over a total period of three consecutive weeks. Please note that sheet 5 could be used with your own clues for other locations – it could be a good idea to create some clues about the school's location. To assist pupils with spellings we suggest that you display a word bank of city names, including the three cities featured in these games.

Our whole world 1

Name: Date:

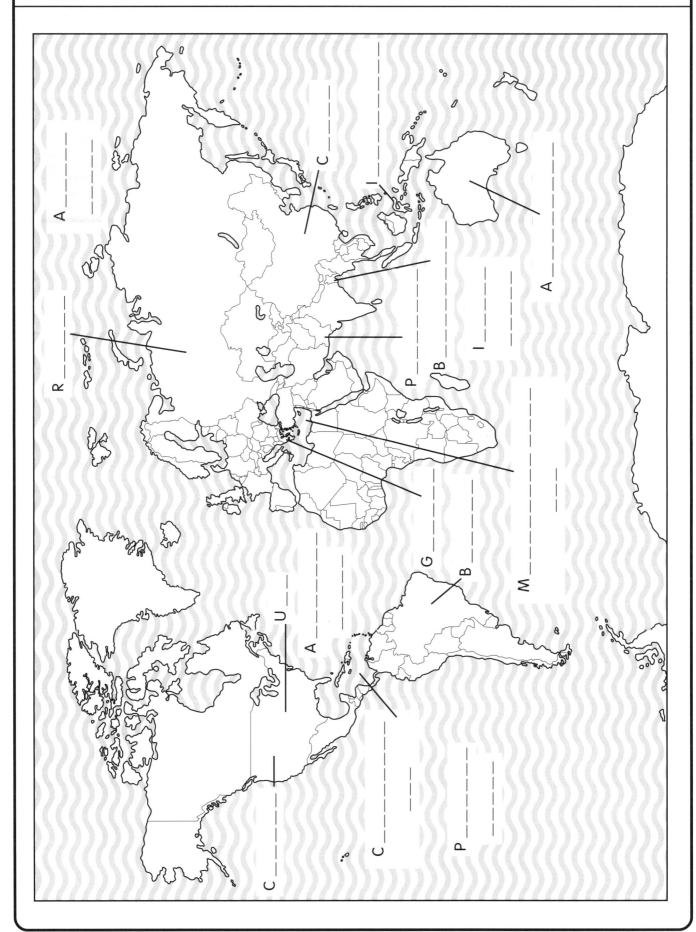

Andrew Brodie: Across the Curriculum Geography 9–10 © A & C Black Publishers Ltd

Our whole world 2

 LITERACY

Name: Date:

Which city is this?   Game 1

 This is a city in Asia.

 It is south of the Tropic of Cancer.

 This city is in a country that juts into an ocean that is named after the country!

 It is a very important city but it is not the capital of the country.

 This city is famous for Bollywood films.

 Lots of people play cricket here.

 This city is located on the Arabian Sea.

 It is built on an island connected to the mainland by many bridges.

 This city has a modern business centre with high-rise buildings near to Chowpatty Beach.

 It used to be known as Bombay.

Our whole world 3

Name: Date:

Which city is this?   Game 2

 This is currently the world's second largest city with a population of 17 million.

 It is in South America.

 This city is south of the Equator.

 It is not on the coast but it is situated near the coast of the Atlantic Ocean.

 This city is very close to the Tropic of Capricorn.

 It is the biggest city in South America.

 It has lots of high-rise buildings.

 Many of the residents are descended from Italian and Japanese immigrants.

 This city is in Brazil.

 It is not the capital city of Brazil.

     Andrew Brodie: Across the Curriculum Geography 9–10 © A & C Black Publishers Ltd

Our whole world 4

LITERACY

Name: Date:

Which city is this?   Game 3

 This city is in the continent of Europe.

 It has many hills and is between three mountains: Mount Parnitha, Mount Pendeli and Mount Hymettos.

 This city is the capital of its country.

 To the south of the city is the Saronic Gulf, part of the Mediterranean Sea.

 One famous place at the top of a hill in the city is called the Acropolis.

 On the Acropolis is a famous building called the Parthenon.

 This city hosted the Olympic Games in 1896 and in 2004.

 Nearly 2500 years ago, three of the world's greatest philosophers lived in this city. Their names were Socrates, Plato and Aristotle.

 Approximately three million people live in this city.

 This city is in Greece.

Our whole world 5

Name: _____ Date: _____

Do you know which city this is?
Here are the clues:

CLUE 1 _____
_____

CLUE 2 _____
_____

CLUE 1 _____
_____

CLUE 2 _____
_____

CLUE 1 _____
_____

CLUE 2 _____
_____

CLUE 1 _____
_____

CLUE 2 _____
_____

CLUE 1 _____
_____

CLUE 2 _____
_____

I think that this city is _____

Geography and numbers

TEACHER'S NOTES

(QCA Unit 25: Geography and numbers)

We have not included a topic web with this unit as the sheets are designed to provide links between geography and numeracy rather than with a wide range of subjects.

Worksheet 1 (**NUMERACY**) provides an introduction to locating places using grid references. The Numeracy Strategy requires Year 5 pupils to be able to use coordinates in the first quadrant and the QCA unit 'Geography and numbers' suggests that pupils in the upper part of primary school should be able to use six-figure grid references. We suggest that pupils should experience the process of using coordinates in the first quadrant then be shown maps, such as those in road atlases, where locations are found by using letters and numbers to identify squares. On our Year 5 worksheets in this unit we introduce the difficult concept of four-figure grid references, before six-figure grid references are introduced in *Across the Curriculum Geography for Ages 10-11*. Children need guidance to understand the convention of using four-figure grid references to represent both the actual spot where the grid lines cross and the square that is to the east and north of the actual coordinate, ie 'to the right and up'. Accordingly, this sheet is designed either for small group use with an adult or for whole class use once it is photocopied on to an OHP transparency. The answers to the questions are as shown on this scaled down grid:

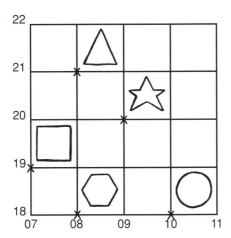

Worksheet 2 (**NUMERACY**) gives pupils the opportunity to practise their use of keys and of four-figure grid references. Each map should look different as the children should add their own features but all the maps should have the following features in common:

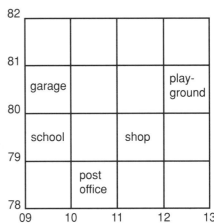

Worksheet 3 (**NUMERACY**) provides further practice of use of four-figure grid references as an extension activity to designing a map. The pupils are provided with a blank grid and are asked to draw a map that must include some coastline and must have the features listed. They should create an appropriate key in the box provided. They should then list the features shown on the map and write the grid reference for each one. As a fun extension activity we have asked them to list these grid references on a separate piece of paper then to ask a partner to find the features represented as quickly as possible – this is probably best as an oral activity so the partner can be timed identifying the correct features.

Geography and numbers 1

Name: Date:

This grid represents part of a grid on a map.

Notice that the bottom left hand corner of a map does not always have the coordinates (0, 0). On this grid the coordinates of the bottom left hand corner are (07, 18).

Notice that every grid line has a two-figure reference: it says 07 not 7, or 08 not 8, etc.

We are going to learn how to show four-figure grid references.

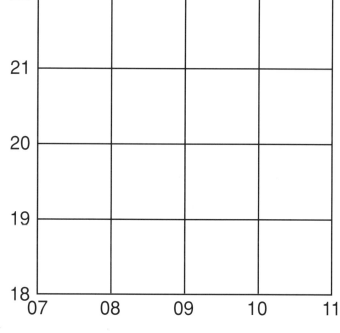

Grid references are like coordinates but we don't show the brackets or the comma between the coordinates. So, the four-figure grid reference for the bottom left-hand corner would be 0718 instead of (07, 18).

Four-figure grid references are very special because they represent a whole square. The grid reference 0718 represents the whole of the square that is to the east and north of the point 0718.

 Practise these four-figure grid references:

Draw a small cross at the point 0920.
Now draw a star in the square 0920.

Draw a small cross at the point 0821.
Now draw a triangle in the square 0821.

Draw a small cross at the point 1018.
Now draw a circle in the square 1018.

Draw a small cross at the point 0719.
Now draw a square in the square 0719.

Draw a small cross at the point 0818.
Now draw a hexagon in the square 0818.

Geography and numbers 2

Name: Date:

 In the key below make up symbols for the features shown.

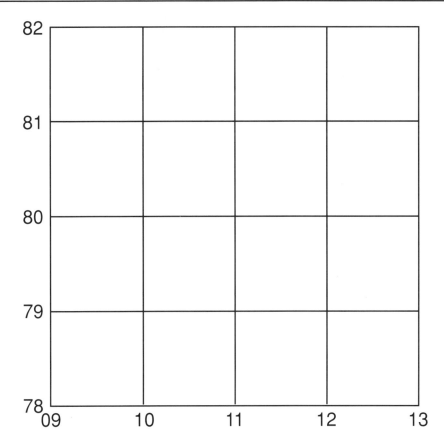

 Draw the symbols on the map at the following grid references:

school 0979
garage 0980
post office 1078
shop 1179
playground 1280

KEY
school
garage
post office
shop
playground

 Now draw at least one road passing through the village shown on your map. You can add other features if you wish to. You may need to write some words on the map: for example, the name of the school or the name of the village. Carefully shade your map using appropriate colours.

Geography and numbers 3

Name: Date:

On the grid below create your own map of an imaginary area.
Label the grid lines with appropriate numbers so that you will be able to use some four-figure grid references.

The map must have some coastline shown and must also include the following features:

      a beach   a promontory   a village   an area of woodland

You can add any other features that you like to make your map as interesting as possible.

On a separate piece of paper list the four-figure grid references of the features shown on your map.

Give your list of grid references to a partner and ask your partner to find the features represented by each one. How quickly can your partner identify all the features?

      Andrew Brodie: Across the Curriculum Geography 9–10 © A & C Black Publishers Ltd